This Book Belongs to:

Help Others With Love!

:OO

Brenda E. Cortz

Children's Organ
Transplant Association®

Partial proceeds from
Howl Gets a Heart go to the
Children's Organ Transplant Association
and Donate Life America.

Howl
Gets a Heart

Written by Brenda E. Cortez
Illustrations by Dindo Contento

Author: Brenda E. Cortez
Howl Gets a Heart
Illustrations & Cover: Dindo Contento
Interior Layout: Marla McKenna

Howl Gets a Heart
ISBN: 978-0-9993601-1-8

Sales Categories:
Children's Books | Growing Up & Facts of Life | Health | Diseases
Children's Books | Growing Up & Facts of Life | Difficult Discussions | Illness
Children's Books | Growing Up & Facts of Life | Health | Visit the Doctor

To my family and friends who have
supported me, especially my husband
Shawn, my daughter Kailey and son Kyle,
my parents, my friend Marla,
the Mielke family, and God above.

In loving memory of Bob Busalacchi,
Maria Cortez and Rose Benecky.
I feel your love and support from Heaven!

Howl is eight years old and just like all the other owls, he loves to have fun and play with his friends whenever he can.

But Howl is a bit different. He was born with a hole in his heart and needs a new healthy, strong heart to stay alive.

Since a heart can't just be bought like toys or candy from a store, Howl and his family have to wait for a new heart, and that's called a donor heart. They feel sad though because a donor heart can't come from a living person like a kidney or liver. This kind of heart has to be donated from a special someone who wants to help another person in need, just like Howl.

Howl's parents actually named him Howl, because it stands for **Help Others With Love!**

Be a
DONOR

Children's Organ
Transplant Association®
www.cota.org

Howl is now feeling worse every day and has been staying at the hospital for almost a month. He has to wear a backpack all the time which has a special machine inside used to pump blood because his own heart can't do that on its own.

Howl asked his mom, "Will I get a new heart soon?"

His mom replied, "Yes, Howl, your name is at the top of the transplant list, so hopefully you will get one any day now!"

Howl stays very hopeful and is learning to have more patience.

Howl warmly hugs his mom and dad, and then he thanks his nurse for bringing him a cold cup of water which helps him feel a little better.

With his I.V. tower in tow, Howl and his dad take a slow walk down the hallway to the hospital playroom so Howl can choose a new bedtime story.

The long wait continues.

After two more weeks, Howl and his family receive the fantastic news they have been eagerly waiting for!

"A heart is now available for Howl," the doctor told them.

Howl is very excited but he is also scared at the same time.

"I'm getting a new heart!" he exclaimed. "And I won't be sick anymore!"

"Yes Howl," said his doctor who will be performing the special transplant surgery. "We will be taking you back to the operating room soon, and you will be given special medicine that will make you feel very sleepy. When you wake up, after your surgery, you will have your new heart."

"Oh Yippee!" screeched Howl. "Will I be able to go home later?"

"No Howl, not right away," replied the doctor. "But hopefully in a week or two you can go home."

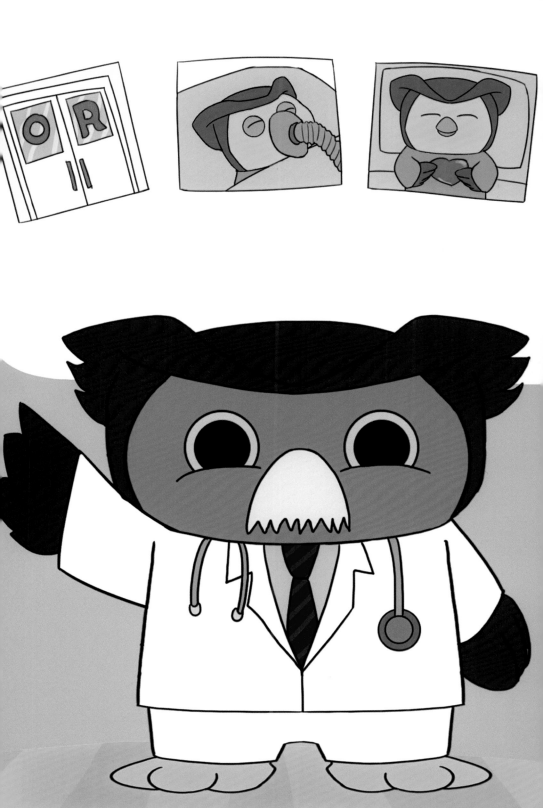

Howl's mom explained, "You won't be feeling that well at first. You will be tired from the surgery, and your body will be adjusting to your new heart."

"Oh, I see," answered Howl. "That's ok, I'm just so happy to be getting a new heart."

"We are too son!" exclaimed Howl's mom and dad. "We are too."

Howl's surgery took seven hours, and his recovery another two weeks, but he is getting much better and feeling like himself again.

"Can I go home soon?" Howl asked his nurse.

"Yes Howl," the doctor said. "You can go home tomorrow," added the nurse.

"Oh good!" Howl cried out happily, "I can't wait to sleep in my own bed, play with my friends and go back to school. I am so very excited!"

Finally at home, Howl looks and feels just like all his other owl friends, except he has to take special medication every day for the rest of his life. This medicine will make sure his new wonderful heart continues to work in his body, and it doesn't reject it.

The medicine isn't Howl's favorite but he knows he has to take it, so he listens to mom and drinks it all gone.

Today, Howl and his mom and dad are meeting the family of the girl who donated her heart to Howl. They are so grateful to her family for thinking of others in their time of sorrow and want to thank them for the generous gift of life. A new heart is a very precious gift. Howl's gift back to his donor family is letting them listen to the heart beating inside of him. It is a very special moment for everyone.

Howl is very happy and thankful for this special gift. He is grateful that someone else believed in organ donation and wanted to *Help Others With Love!*

9 inch plush Howl makes a
great book buddy!
Available at:
donatelife.net/books

Other books by Brenda Cortez:

My Mom is Having Surgery

Coming Soon:

Howl Helps Bella

Howl Learns About Dialysis

Howl Helps Others With Love

GLOSSARY:

Heart Transplant – A procedure that replaces a patient's failing or injured heart with a heart from an organ donor

IV Tower – A metal tower that holds a bag of liquid medication which flows directly into a patients veins

Organ Donor – A person who is willing to give a body organ they no longer need to save another person's life

Organ Donation – The process of surgically removing an organ or tissue from one person (the organ donor) and placing it into another person (the recipient)

Operating Room – A room in a hospital that is specially equipped for surgery

Rejection – Does not take or accept. In the case of an organ transplant, a person's body may not take or accept the new organ

Surgery – A medical procedure to treat a disease or fix an injury

Transplant List – A list of people in the United States who are waiting for a life-saving organ

Transplant Recipient – A person who receives an organ from another person